The Far Side™

Theme·a·Month

1999
Desk Calendar

Gary Larson

The Ink Group

Web Site: http://www.inkgroup.com

Published and distributed by The Ink Group
Printed in Hong Kong

AUSTRALIA
The Ink Group Pty Ltd Publishers
111 Burrows Road, Alexandria
NSW 2015 Australia
Telephone: + 61 2 9950 9777
Facsimile: + 61 2 9557 8965

UNITED KINGDOM
The Ink Group Publishers Limited
3 The Quadrillion, Westmead Drive
Swindon, Wiltshire SN5 7TH England
Telephone: + 44 1793 491 878
Facsimile: + 44 1793 491 877

NEW ZEALAND
The Ink Group NZ Limited
Unit B, 8 Piermark Drive, North Harbour
Albany, Auckland, New Zealand
Telephone: + 64 9 415 5529
Facsimile: + 64 9 415 5603

"Hey, why are there four safari cartoons in September?"

Because it's "Where's My Pith Helmet?" month, featuring the curious escapades of explorers and anthropologists. We've taken a new approach to this year's *Far Side* ™ *Desk Calendar*, identifying twelve frequent subjects from the odd world of The Far Side ™ and celebrating each one for an entire month! It means that after you trek through June with the mouth-watering exploits of various carnivores ("Tastes Like Chicken"), you'll discover that July promises four classic cow cartoons ("Four Stomachs, No Waiting"). You'll also find months honoring scientists ("Hands Off My Bunsen Burner"), the Old West ("Get Off Your High Horse"), Hell ("Is It Hot in Here, or Is It Just Me?"), and many more. The best part is that each theme is introduced by a never-before-seen cartoon drawn by Gary Larson especially for the 1999 calendars. So, if you fit anywhere in between an extra-terrestrial and a mobster, this calendar is for you.

January

Sunday	Monday	Tuesday	Wednesday	Thursday	Friday	Saturday
27	28	29	30	31	1 *New Year's Day* *Kwanzaa ends (USA)*	2
3	4	5	6 *Epiphany*	7	8	9
10	11	12	13	14	15 *Coming of Age Day (Japan)*	16
17	18 *Martin Luther King Jr's Birthday observed (USA)* *Ramadan ends*	19	20	21	22	23
24	25	26 *Australia Day*	27	28	29	30
31						

Notes

December '98

S	M	T	W	T	F	S
		1	2	3	4	5
6	7	8	9	10	11	12
13	14	15	16	17	18	19
20	21	22	23	24	25	26
27	28	29	30	31		

February

S	M	T	W	T	F	S
	1	2	3	4	5	6
7	8	9	10	11	12	13
14	15	16	17	18	19	20
21	22	23	24	25	26	27
28						

"Hey, everyone! Simmons here just uttered a discouraging word!"

January

Monday	December 28

Tuesday	29

Wednesday	30

Thursday	31

Friday	1

New Year's Day
Kwanzaa ends (USA)

Saturday	2

Sunday	3

S	M	T	W	T	F	S
27	28	29	30	31	1	2
3	4	5	6	7	8	9
10	11	12	13	14	15	16
17	18	19	20	21	22	23
24 / 31	25	26	27	28	29	30

"Vince! Just trample him! ... He's drawing you into his kind of fight!"

January

Monday   4

Tuesday   5

Wednesday   6

Epiphany

Thursday   7

Friday   8

Saturday   9

Sunday   10

S	M	T	W	T	F	S
					1	2
3	4	5	6	7	8	9
10	11	12	13	14	15	16
17	18	19	20	21	22	23
24 31	25	26	27	28	29	30

Trying to calm the herd, Jake himself was suddenly awestruck by the image of beauty and unbridled fury on the cliff above—Pink Shadow had returned.

January

Monday   11

Tuesday   12

Wednesday   13

Thursday   14

Friday   15

Coming of Age Day (Japan)

Saturday   16

Sunday   17

S	M	T	W	T	F	S
					1	2
3	4	5	6	7	8	9
10	11	12	13	14	15	16
17	18	19	20	21	22	23
24 31	25	26	27	28	29	30

"Hey! Look at me, everybody! I'm a cowboy! ... Howdy, howdy, howdy!"

January

Monday   **18**

Martin Luther King Jr's
Birthday observed (USA)
Ramadan ends

Tuesday   **19**

Wednesday   **20**

Thursday   **21**

Friday   **22**

Saturday   **23**

S	M	T	W	T	F	S
27	28	29	30	31	1	2
3	4	5	6	7	8	9
10	11	12	13	14	15	16
17	18	19	20	21	22	23
24 31	25	26	27	28	29	30

Sunday   **24**

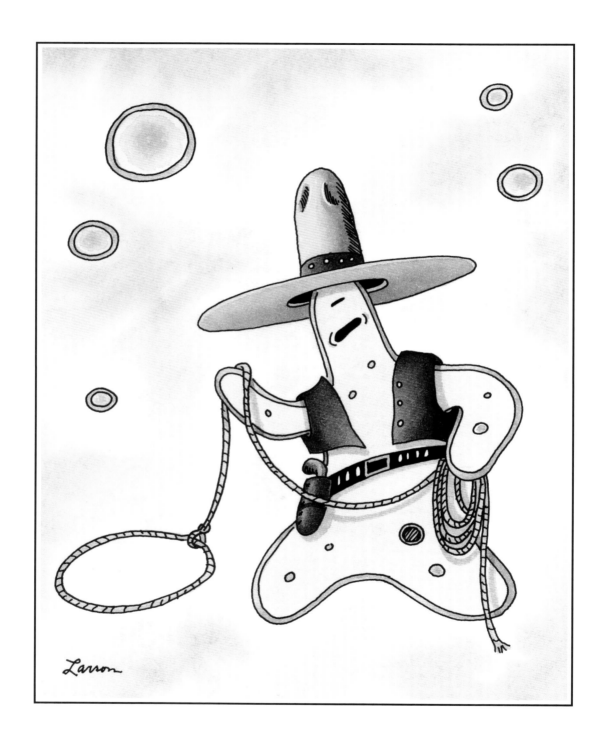

"So, until next week—adios, amoebas."

January

Monday 25

Tuesday 26

Australia Day

Wednesday 27

Thursday 28

Friday 29

Saturday 30

Sunday 31

S	M	T	W	T	F	S
					1	2
3	4	5	6	7	8	9
10	11	12	13	14	15	16
17	18	19	20	21	22	23
24 31	25	26	27	28	29	30

February

Sunday	Monday	Tuesday	Wednesday	Thursday	Friday	Saturday
31	1	2	3	4	5	6
		Groundhog Day (USA)				Waitangi Day (New Zealand)
7	8	9	10	11	12	13
				National Foundation Day (Japan)		
14	15	16	17	18	19	20
St Valentine's Day	Presidents' Day (USA) Lunar New Year - Year of the Rabbit		Ash Wednesday			
21	22	23	24	25	26	27
28	1	2	3	4	5	6

Notes

January

S	M	T	W	T	F	S
27	28	29	30	31	1	2
3	4	5	6	7	8	9
10	11	12	13	14	15	16
17	18	19	20	21	22	23
24 31	25	26	27	28	29	30

March

S	M	T	W	T	F	S
28	1	2	3	4	5	6
7	8	9	10	11	12	13
14	15	16	17	18	19	20
21	22	23	24	25	26	27
28	29	30	31	1	2	3

"The picture's pretty bleak, gentlemen. ... The world's climates are changing, the mammals are taking over, and we all have a brain about the size of a walnut."

February

Monday   **1**

Tuesday   **2**

Groundhog Day (USA)

Wednesday   **3**

Thursday   **4**

Friday   **5**

Saturday   **6**

Waitangi Day (New Zealand)

Sunday   **7**

S	M	T	W	T	F	S
	1	2	3	4	5	6
7	8	9	10	11	12	13
14	15	16	17	18	19	20
21	22	23	24	25	26	27
28						

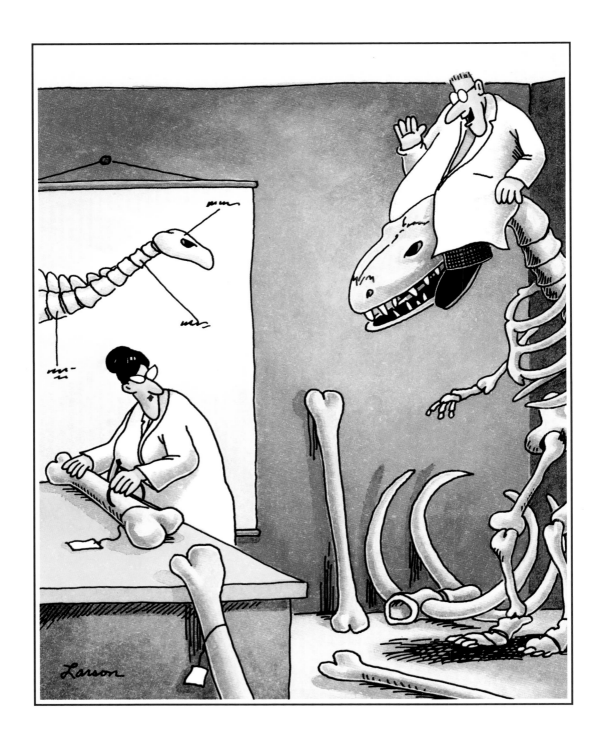

"Hi. ... Hi, Miss Collins."

February

Monday   8

Tuesday   9

Wednesday   10

Thursday   11

National Foundation Day
(Japan)

Friday   12

Saturday   13

S	M	T	W	T	F	S
31	1	2	3	4	5	6
7	8	9	10	11	12	13
14	15	16	17	18	19	20
21	22	23	24	25	26	27
28	1	2	3	4	5	6

Sunday   14

St Valentine's Day

An instant later, both Professor Waxman and his time machine are obliterated, leaving the cold-blooded/warm-blooded dinosaur debate still unresolved.

February

Monday   **15**

Presidents' Day (USA)
Lunar New Year -
Year of the Rabbit

Tuesday   **16**

Wednesday   **17**

Ash Wednesday

Thursday   **18**

Friday   **19**

Saturday   **20**

S	M	T	W	T	F	S
31	1	2	3	4	5	6
7	8	9	10	11	12	13
14	15	16	17	18	19	20
21	22	23	24	25	26	27
28	1	2	3	4	5	6

Sunday   **21**

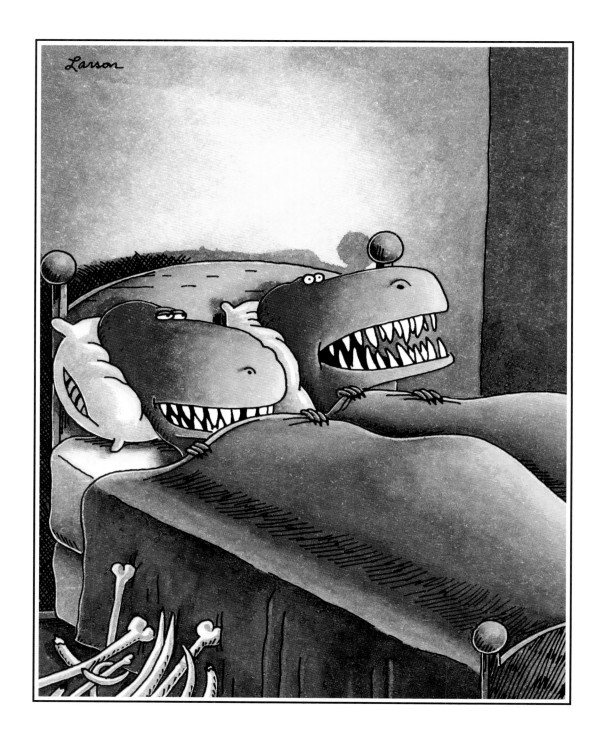

"Wait a minute here. ... Did I floss?"

February

Monday	22

Tuesday	23

Wednesday	24

Thursday	25

Friday	26

Saturday	27

Sunday	28

S	M	T	W	T	F	S
31	1	2	3	4	5	6
7	8	9	10	11	12	13
14	15	16	17	18	19	20
21	22	23	24	25	26	27
28	1	2	3	4	5	6

March

Sunday	Monday	Tuesday	Wednesday	Thursday	Friday	Saturday
28	1 First Day of Autumn (Southern Hemisphere) Labour Day (Australia-WA)	2 Purim	3	4	5	6
7	8 International Women's Day Labour Day (Australia-VIC)	9	10	11	12	13
14 Mothering Sunday (UK, Ireland)	15 Canberra Day (Australia-ACT)	16	17 St Patrick's Day	18	19	20 Vernal Equinox (Northern Hemisphere)
21	22	23	24	25 The Annunciation	26	27 Daylight Saving ends (Australia-NSW, ACT, VIC, TAS, SA)
28 Palm Sunday	29	30	31	1	2	3

Notes

"Well, here they come. ... You locked the keys inside, you do the talkin'."

March

Monday   1

First Day of Autumn
(Southern Hemisphere)
Labour Day (Australia-WA)

Tuesday   2

Purim

Wednesday   3

Thursday   4

Friday   5

Saturday   6

S	M	T	W	T	F	S
28	1	2	3	4	5	6
7	8	9	10	11	12	13
14	15	16	17	18	19	20
21	22	23	24	25	26	27
28	29	30	31	1	2	3

Sunday   7

"Now don't forget, Gorok! ... *This* time punch some holes in the lid!"

March

Monday   8

International Women's Day
Labour Day (Australia-VIC)

Tuesday   9

Wednesday   10

Thursday   11

Friday   12

Saturday   13

Sunday   14

Mothering Sunday
(UK, Ireland)

S	M	T	W	T	F	S
28	1	2	3	4	5	6
7	8	9	10	11	12	13
14	15	16	17	18	19	20
21	22	23	24	25	26	27
28	29	30	31	1	2	3

"Ooooooooooooooo!"

March

Monday   15

Canberra Day (Australia-ACT)

Tuesday   16

Wednesday   17

St Patrick's Day

Thursday   18

Friday   19

Saturday   20

Vernal Equinox
(Northern Hemisphere)

Sunday   21

S	M	T	W	T	F	S
28	1	2	3	4	5	6
7	8	9	10	11	12	13
14	15	16	17	18	19	20
21	22	23	24	25	26	27
28	29	30	31	1	2	3

March

Monday   22

Tuesday   23

Wednesday   24

Thursday   25

The Annunciation

Friday   26

Saturday   27

Daylight Saving ends
(Australia-NSW, ACT, VIC, TAS, SA)
Summer Time begins (Europe)

Sunday   28

Palm Sunday

S	M	T	W	T	F	S
	1	2	3	4	5	6
7	8	9	10	11	12	13
14	15	16	17	18	19	20
21	22	23	24	25	26	27
28	29	30	31			

April

Sunday	Monday	Tuesday	Wednesday	Thursday	Friday	Saturday
28	29	30	31	1 April Fool's Day Passover begins	2 Good Friday	3
4 Easter Sunday	5 Easter Monday	6	7	8	9	10
11 Orthodox Easter Day	12	13	14	15	16	17 Islamic New Year
18	19	20	21	22	23 St George's Day (England, Canada)	24
25 Anzac Day (Australia, New Zealand) Liberation Day (Italy)	26 Anzac Day Holiday	27	28 Greenery Day (Japan)	29	30	1

Notes

March
S	M	T	W	T	F	S
28	1	2	3	4	5	6
7	8	9	10	11	12	13
14	15	16	17	18	19	20
21	22	23	24	25	26	27
28	29	30	31	1	2	3

May
S	M	T	W	T	F	S
25	26	27	28	29	30	1
2	3	4	5	6	7	8
9	10	11	12	13	14	15
16	17	18	19	20	21	22
23	24	25	26	27	28	29
30	31					

"Just keep starin', buddy, and I'll show ya my *bad* eye!"

April

Monday   March 29

Tuesday   30

Wednesday   31

Thursday   1

April Fool's Day
Passover begins

Friday   2

Good Friday

Saturday   3

Sunday   4

Easter Sunday
Daylight Saving begins
(Canada, USA-except Arizona, Hawaii, Indiana)

S	M	T	W	T	F	S
28	29	30	31	1	2	3
4	5	6	7	8	9	10
11	12	13	14	15	16	17
18	19	20	21	22	23	24
25	26	27	28	29	30	

"Uh-oh, Lorraine. ... Someone seems to be checking you out."

April

Monday 5

Easter Monday

Tuesday 6

Wednesday 7

Thursday 8

Friday 9

Saturday 10

Sunday 11

Orthodox Easter Day

S	M	T	W	T	F	S
28	29	30	31	1	2	3
4	5	6	7	8	9	10
11	12	13	14	15	16	17
18	19	20	21	22	23	24
25	26	27	28	29	30	1

"And here he is—but when I started, I bet he was at least this tall."

April

Monday	12

Tuesday	13

Wednesday	14

Thursday	15

Friday	16

Saturday	17

Islamic New Year

Sunday	18

S	M	T	W	T	F	S
				1	2	3
4	5	6	7	8	9	10
11	12	13	14	15	16	17
18	19	20	21	22	23	24
25	26	27	28	29	30	

"Just back off, buddy...unless you want a fat lip."

April

Monday   19

Tuesday   20

Wednesday   21

Thursday   22

Friday   23

St George's Day
(England, Canada)

Saturday   24

Sunday   25

Anzac Day
(Australia, New Zealand)
Liberation Day (Italy)

S	M	T	W	T	F	S
28	29	30	31	1	2	3
4	5	6	7	8	9	10
11	12	13	14	15	16	17
18	19	20	21	22	23	24
25	26	27	28	29	30	1

May

Sunday	Monday	Tuesday	Wednesday	Thursday	Friday	Saturday
25	26	27	28	29	30	1 Labour Day (Brazil, France, Hungary, Switzerland, Sweden) May Day (Germany, Finland)
2	3 Labour Day (Australia-QLD) May Day (Australia-NT) Early May Bank Holiday (UK) Constitution Memorial Day (Japan)	4	5	6	7	8 Victory Day (France)
9 Mother's Day (Australia, New Zealand, USA, Canada, Japan)	10	11	12	13 Ascension Day (Canada, Denmark, France, Finland, Germany, Netherlands, Switzerland, Sweden)	14	15 Armed Forces' Day (USA)
16	17	18	19	20	21 Shavuot begins	22 Shavuot ends
23 Pentecost (Whitsunday)	24 Victoria Day (Canada)	25	26	27	28	29
30 Trinity Sunday	31 Memorial Day (USA) Spring Bank Holiday (UK)					

Notes

April
S	M	T	W	T	F	S
				1	2	3
4	5	6	7	8	9	10
11	12	13	14	15	16	17
18	19	20	21	22	23	24
25	26	27	28	29	30	

June
S	M	T	W	T	F	S
		1	2	3	4	5
6	7	8	9	10	11	12
13	14	15	16	17	18	19
20	21	22	23	24	25	26
27	28	29	30			

"Eraser fight!!"

May

Monday *April* 26

Anzac Day Holiday

Tuesday 27

Wednesday 28

Greenery Day (Japan)

Thursday 29

Friday 30

Saturday 1

Labour Day
(Brazil, France, Hungary, Switzerland, Sweden)
May Day (Germany, Finland)

Sunday 2

S	M	T	W	T	F	S
25	26	27	28	29	30	1
2	3	4	5	6	7	8
9	10	11	12	13	14	15
16	17	18	19	20	21	22
23 / 30	24 / 31	25	26	27	28	29

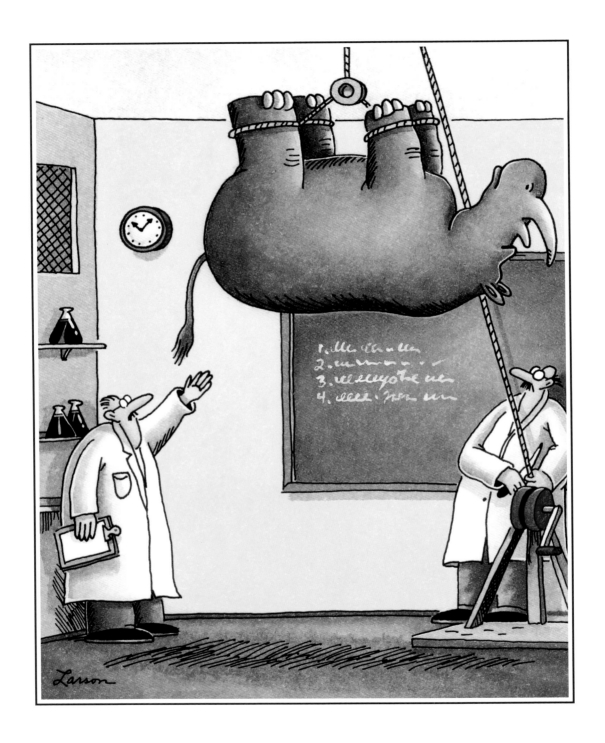

Testing whether or not rhinos land on their feet

May

Monday 3

Labour Day (Australia-QLD)
May Day (Australia-NT)
Early May Bank Holiday (UK)
Constitution Memorial Day (Japan)

Tuesday 4

Wednesday 5

Thursday 6

Friday 7

Saturday 8

Victory Day (France)

Sunday 9

Mother's Day
(Australia, New Zealand,
USA, Canada, Japan)

S	M	T	W	T	F	S
25	26	27	28	29	30	1
2	3	4	5	6	7	8
9	10	11	12	13	14	15
16	17	18	19	20	21	22
23 30	24 31	25	26	27	28	29

May

Monday   10

Tuesday   11

Wednesday   12

Thursday   13

Ascension Day
(Canada, Denmark, France, Finland, Germany,
Netherlands, Switzerland, Sweden)

Friday   14

Saturday   15

Armed Forces' Day (USA)

Sunday   16

S	M	T	W	T	F	S
25	26	27	28	29	30	1
2	3	4	5	6	7	8
9	10	11	12	13	14	15
16	17	18	19	20	21	22
23	24	25	26	27	28	29
30	31					

Einstein discovers that time is actually money.

May

Monday   17

Tuesday   18

Wednesday   19

Thursday   20

Friday   21

Shavuot begins

Saturday   22

Shavuot ends

Sunday   23

Pentecost (Whitsunday)

S	M	T	W	T	F	S
						1
2	3	4	5	6	7	8
9	10	11	12	13	14	15
16	17	18	19	20	21	22
23 30	24 31	25	26	27	28	29

"And notice, gentlemen, the faster I go, the more Simmons sounds like a motorboat."

May

Monday 24

Victoria Day (Canada)

Tuesday 25

Wednesday 26

Thursday 27

Friday 28

Saturday 29

Sunday 30

Trinity Sunday

S	M	T	W	T	F	S
25	26	27	28	29	30	1
2	3	4	5	6	7	8
9	10	11	12	13	14	15
16	17	18	19	20	21	22
23 30	24 31	25	26	27	28	29

June

Sunday	Monday	Tuesday	Wednesday	Thursday	Friday	Saturday
30	31	1 First Day of Winter (Southern Hemisphere)	2	3 Corpus Christi	4	5
6	7 Queen's Birthday (New Zealand)	8	9	10	11	12
13	14 Queen's Birthday (Australia-except WA) Flag Day (USA)	15	16	17	18	19
20 Father's Day (USA, UK, Ireland, Canada, Japan)	21 Summer Solstice (Northern Hemisphere)	22	23	24 St-Jean-Baptiste Day (Canada)	25	26
27	28	29	30			

Notes

May

S	M	T	W	T	F	S
						1
2	3	4	5	6	7	8
9	10	11	12	13	14	15
16	17	18	19	20	21	22
23 30	24 31	25	26	27	28	29

July

S	M	T	W	T	F	S
				1	2	3
4	5	6	7	8	9	10
11	12	13	14	15	16	17
18	19	20	21	22	23	24
25	26	27	28	29	30	31

"Don't be alarmed, folks. ... He's completely harmless unless something startles him."

June

Monday   Mar 31

Memorial Day (USA)
Spring Bank Holiday (UK)

Tuesday   1

First Day of Winter
(Southern Hemisphere)

Wednesday   2

Thursday   3

Corpus Christi

Friday   4

Saturday   5

Sunday   6

S	M	T	W	T	F	S
30	31	1	2	3	4	5
6	7	8	9	10	11	12
13	14	15	16	17	18	19
20	21	22	23	24	25	26
27	28	29	30	1	2	3

Impolite as they were, the other bears could never help staring at Larry's enormous deer gut.

June

Monday   7

Queen's Birthday
(New Zealand)

Tuesday   8

Wednesday   9

Thursday   10

Friday   11

Saturday   12

S	M	T	W	T	F	S
30	31	1	2	3	4	5
6	7	8	9	10	11	12
13	14	15	16	17	18	19
20	21	22	23	24	25	26
27	28	29	30	1	2	3

Sunday   13

"And here we are last summer off the coast of ... Helen, is this Hawaii or Florida?"

June

Monday 14

Queen's Birthday
(Australia-except WA)
Flag Day (USA)

Tuesday 15

Wednesday 16

Thursday 17

Friday 18

Saturday 19

Sunday 20

Father's Day
(USA, UK, Ireland,
Canada, Japan)

S	M	T	W	T	F	S
30	31	1	2	3	4	5
6	7	8	9	10	11	12
13	14	15	16	17	18	19
20	21	22	23	24	25	26
27	28	29	30	1	2	3

"Well, so much for the unicorns. ... But, from now on, all carnivores will be confined to 'C' deck."

June

Monday 21

Summer Solstice
(Northern Hemisphere)

Tuesday 22

Wednesday 23

Thursday 24

St-Jean-Baptiste Day (Canada)

Friday 25

Saturday 26

Sunday 27

S	M	T	W	T	F	S
30	31	1	2	3	4	5
6	7	8	9	10	11	12
13	14	15	16	17	18	19
20	21	22	23	24	25	26
27	28	29	30	1	2	3

July

Sunday	Monday	Tuesday	Wednesday	Thursday	Friday	Saturday
27	28	29	30	1 Canada Day HKSAR Establishment Day (Hong Kong)	2	3
4 Independence Day (USA)	5	6	7	8	9	10
11	12 Battle of the Boyne (Northern Ireland)	13	14 Bastille Day (France)	15	16	17
18	19	20	21	22	23	24
25	26	27	28	29	30	31

Notes

June

S	M	T	W	T	F	S
30	31	1	2	3	4	5
6	7	8	9	10	11	12
13	14	15	16	17	18	19
20	21	22	23	24	25	26
27	28	29	30			

August

S	M	T	W	T	F	S
1	2	3	4	5	6	7
8	9	10	11	12	13	14
15	16	17	18	19	20	21
22	23	24	25	26	27	28
29	30	31				

"You're sick, Jessy! ... Sick, sick, sick!"

July

Monday June 28

Tuesday 29

Wednesday 30

Thursday 1

Canada Day
HKSAR Establishment Day (Hong Kong)

Friday 2

Saturday 3

S	M	T	W	T	F	S
				1	2	3
4	5	6	7	8	9	10
11	12	13	14	15	16	17
18	19	20	21	22	23	24
25	26	27	28	29	30	31

Sunday 4

Independence Day (USA)

July

Monday   5

Tuesday   6

Wednesday   7

Thursday   8

Friday   9

Saturday   10

Sunday   11

S	M	T	W	T	F	S
27	28	29	30	1	2	3
4	5	6	7	8	9	10
11	12	13	14	15	16	17
18	19	20	21	22	23	24
25	26	27	28	29	30	31

How cow documentaries are made

July

Monday 12

Battle of the Boyne (Northern Ireland)

Tuesday 13

Wednesday 14

Bastille Day (France)

Thursday 15

Friday 16

Saturday 17

Sunday 18

S	M	T	W	T	F	S
				1	2	3
4	5	6	7	8	9	10
11	12	13	14	15	16	17
18	19	20	21	22	23	24
25	26	27	28	29	30	31

"Ooo! *This* is always amusing. ... Here comes Bessie inside her plastic cow ball."

July

Monday	19
Tuesday	20
Wednesday	21
Thursday	22
Friday	23
Saturday	24
Sunday	25

S	M	T	W	T	F	S
27	28	29	30	1	2	3
4	5	6	7	8	9	10
11	12	13	14	15	16	17
18	19	20	21	22	23	24
25	26	27	28	29	30	31

August

Sunday	Monday	Tuesday	Wednesday	Thursday	Friday	Saturday
1 Swiss National Day Horses' Birthday	2 Civic Holiday (Canada)	3	4	5	6	7
8	9	10	11	12	13	14
15 Assumption (France, Germany, Canada, Italy) Dormition of Our Lady (Greek Orthodox Church)	16	17	18	19	20	21
22	23	24	25	26	27	28
29	30 Summer Bank Holiday (UK)	31	1	2	3	4

Notes

July

S	M	T	W	T	F	S
27	28	29	30	1	2	3
4	5	6	7	8	9	10
11	12	13	14	15	16	17
18	19	20	21	22	23	24
25	26	27	28	29	30	31

September

S	M	T	W	T	F	S
			1	2	3	4
5	6	7	8	9	10	11
12	13	14	15	16	17	18
19	20	21	22	23	24	25
26	27	28	29	30		

IS It Hot in Here, or IS It Just Me?

Despite his repeated efforts to explain things to her, Satan could never dissuade his mother from offering cookies and milk to the accursed.

August

Monday   July 26

Tuesday   27

Wednesday   28

Thursday   29

Friday   30

Saturday   31

Sunday   1

Swiss National Day
Horses' Birthday

S	M	T	W	T	F	S
1	2	3	4	5	6	7
8	9	10	11	12	13	14
15	16	17	18	19	20	21
22	23	24	25	26	27	28
29	30	31	1	2	3	4

"For crying out loud! Look at this place! ...Well, this is one little Satanic ritual that's coming to an end!"

August

Monday   2

Civic Holiday (Canada)

Tuesday   3

Wednesday   4

Thursday   5

Friday   6

Saturday   7

S	M	T	W	T	F	S
1	2	3	4	5	6	7
8	9	10	11	12	13	14
15	16	17	18	19	20	21
22	23	24	25	26	27	28
29	30	31				

Sunday   8

Hell's cafeteria

August

Monday   9

Tuesday   10

Wednesday   11

Thursday   12

Friday   13

Saturday   14

Sunday   15

Assumption (France,
Germany, Canada, Italy)
Dormition of Our Lady
(Greek Orthodox Church)

S	M	T	W	T	F	S
1	2	3	4	5	6	7
8	9	10	11	12	13	14
15	16	17	18	19	20	21
22	23	24	25	26	27	28
29	30	31	1	2	3	4

August

Monday   16

Tuesday   17

Wednesday   18

Thursday   19

Friday   20

Saturday   21

S	M	T	W	T	F	S
1	2	3	4	5	6	7
8	9	10	11	12	13	14
15	16	17	18	19	20	21
22	23	24	25	26	27	28
29	30	31				

Sunday   22

"OK, sir, would you like inferno or non-inferno? ... Ha! Just kidding. It's all inferno, of course—I just get a kick out of saying that."

August

Notes

Monday	23

Tuesday	24

Wednesday	25

Thursday	26

Friday	27

Saturday	28

Sunday	29

S	M	T	W	T	F	S
1	2	3	4	5	6	7
8	9	10	11	12	13	14
15	16	17	18	19	20	21
22	23	24	25	26	27	28
29	30	31	1	2	3	4

September

Sunday	Monday	Tuesday	Wednesday	Thursday	Friday	Saturday
29	30	31	1	2	3	4
			First Day of Spring (Southern Hemisphere)			
5	6	7	8	9	10	11
Father's Day (Australia, New Zealand)	Labor Day (USA, Canada)					Rosh Hashanah
12	13	14	15	16	17	18
Rosh Hashanah			Respect for the Aged Day (Japan)			
19	20	21	22	23	24	25
	Yom Kippur			Autumnal Equinox (Northern Hemisphere)		First Day of Tabernacles
26	27	28	29	30		
Second Day of Tabernacles	Queen's Birthday (Australia-WA)					

Notes

August

S	M	T	W	T	F	S
1	2	3	4	5	6	7
8	9	10	11	12	13	14
15	16	17	18	19	20	21
22	23	24	25	26	27	28
29	30	31				

October

S	M	T	W	T	F	S
					1	2
3	4	5	6	7	8	9
10	11	12	13	14	15	16
17	18	19	20	21	22	23
24 31	25	26	27	28	29	30

Murray is caught desecrating the secret appliance burial grounds.

September

Monday   *August* 30

Summer Bank Holiday (UK)

Tuesday   31

Wednesday   1

First Day of Spring
(Southern Hemisphere)

Thursday   2

Friday   3

Saturday   4

Sunday   5

Father's Day (Australia, New Zealand)

S	M	T	W	T	F	S
29	30	31	1	2	3	4
5	6	7	8	9	10	11
12	13	14	15	16	17	18
19	20	21	22	23	24	25
26	27	28	29	30	1	2

"Not too close, Higgins. ... This one's got a knife."

September

Monday   6

Labor Day (USA, Canada)

Tuesday   7

Wednesday   8

Thursday   9

Friday   10

Saturday   11

Rosh Hashanah

Sunday   12

Rosh Hashanah

S	M	T	W	T	F	S
29	30	31	1	2	3	4
5	6	7	8	9	10	11
12	13	14	15	16	17	18
19	20	21	22	23	24	25
26	27	28	29	30	1	2

"Oh my gosh, Andrew! Don't eat those! ... Those are *poison* arrows!"

September

Monday   13

Tuesday   14

Wednesday   15

Respect for the Aged Day (Japan)

Thursday   16

Friday   17

Saturday   18

S	M	T	W	T	F	S
29	30	31	1	2	3	4
5	6	7	8	9	10	11
12	13	14	15	16	17	18
19	20	21	22	23	24	25
26	27	28	29	30		

Sunday   19

Jungle apparel

September

Monday	20

Yom Kippur

Tuesday	21

Wednesday	22

Thursday	23

Autumnal Equinox
(Northern Hemisphere)

Friday	24

Saturday	25

First Day of Tabernacles

Sunday	26

Second Day of Tabernacles

S	M	T	W	T	F	S
29	30	31	1	2	3	4
5	6	7	8	9	10	11
12	13	14	15	16	17	18
19	20	21	22	23	24	25
26	27	28	29	30	1	2

October

Sunday	Monday	Tuesday	Wednesday	Thursday	Friday	Saturday
26	27	28	29	30	1	2
					National Day (China)	
3 Daylight Saving begins (Australia-TAS) Day of German Unity	4 Labour Day (Australia-NSW, ACT, SA)	5	6	7	8	9
10	11 Thanksgiving Day (Canada) Columbus Day (USA)	12	13	14	15	16
17	18	19	20	21	22	23
24	25 Labour Day (New zealand)	26	27	28	29	30
31 Halloween						

Notes

September						
S	M	T	W	T	F	S
29	30	31	1	2	3	4
5	6	7	8	9	10	11
12	13	14	15	16	17	18
19	20	21	22	23	24	25
26	27	28	29	30		

November						
S	M	T	W	T	F	S
31	1	2	3	4	5	6
7	8	9	10	11	12	13
14	15	16	17	18	19	20
21	22	23	24	25	26	27
28	29	30				

"We've got the murder weapon and the motive. ... Now if we can just establish time of death."

October

Monday   *September* 27

Queen's Birthday (Australia-WA)

Tuesday   28

Wednesday   29

Thursday   30

Friday   1

National Day (China)

Saturday   2

Sunday   3

Daylight Saving begins (Australia-TAS)
Day of German Unity

S	M	T	W	T	F	S
26	27	28	29	30	1	2
3	4	5	6	7	8	9
10	11	12	13	14	15	16
17	18	19	20	21	22	23
24 31	25	26	27	28	29	30

Primitive mobsters

October

Monday   4

Labour Day (Australia-NSW, ACT, SA)

Tuesday   5

Wednesday   6

Thursday   7

Friday   8

Saturday   9

S	M	T	W	T	F	S
26	27	28	29	30	1	2
3	4	5	6	7	8	9
10	11	12	13	14	15	16
17	18	19	20	21	22	23
24 31	25	26	27	28	29	30

Sunday   10

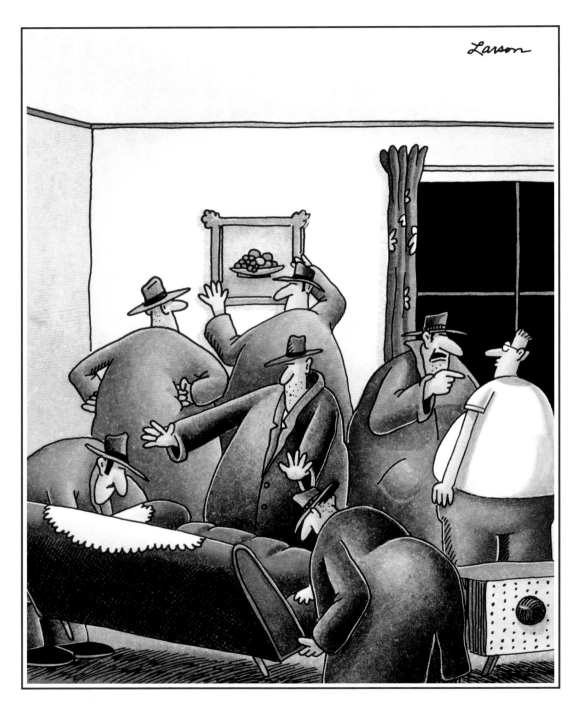

"The boss wants his money, see? Or next time it won't be just your living room we rearrange."

October

Monday 11

Thanksgiving Day (Canada)
Columbus Day (USA)

Tuesday 12

Wednesday 13

Thursday 14

Friday 15

Saturday 16

Sunday 17

S	M	T	W	T	F	S
26	27	28	29	30	1	2
3	4	5	6	7	8	9
10	11	12	13	14	15	16
17	18	19	20	21	22	23
24 31	25	26	27	28	29	30

"Aha! The murderer's footprints! 'Course, we all leave tracks like this."

October

Monday   18

Tuesday   19

Wednesday   20

Thursday   21

Friday   22

Saturday   23

Sunday   24

S	M	T	W	T	F	S
26	27	28	29	30	1	2
3	4	5	6	7	8	9
10	11	12	13	14	15	16
17	18	19	20	21	22	23
24 / 31	25	26	27	28	29	30

Lizard thugs

October

Monday   25

Labour Day (New Zealand)

Tuesday   26

Wednesday   27

Thursday   28

Friday   29

Saturday   30

S	M	T	W	T	F	S
26	27	28	29	30	1	2
3	4	5	6	7	8	9
10	11	12	13	14	15	16
17	18	19	20	21	22	23
24 31	25	26	27	28	29	30

Sunday   31

Halloween
Daylight Saving begins (Australia-NSW, ACT, Vic, SA)
Summer Time ends (Europe)
Daylight Saving ends (Canada, USA-except Arizona, Hawaii, Indiana)

November

Sunday	Monday	Tuesday	Wednesday	Thursday	Friday	Saturday
31	1	2	3	4	5	6
	All Saints' Day	All Souls' Day Election Day (USA)				
7	8	9	10	11	12	13
				Armistice Day Remembrance Day (Canada) Veterans' Day (USA)		
14	15	16	17	18	19	20
			Day of Repentance and Prayer (Germany)			
21	22	23	24	25	26	27
				Thanksgiving Day (USA)		
28	29	30	1	2	3	4
First Sunday in Advent						

Notes

October

S	M	T	W	T	F	S
26	27	28	29	30	1	2
3	4	5	6	7	8	9
10	11	12	13	14	15	16
17	18	19	20	21	22	23
24 31	25	26	27	28	29	30

December

S	M	T	W	T	F	S
28	29	30	1	2	3	4
5	6	7	8	9	10	11
12	13	14	15	16	17	18
19	20	21	22	23	24	25
26	27	28	29	30	31	

November

Notes

Monday   1

All Saints' Day

Tuesday   2

All Souls' Day
Election Day (USA)

Wednesday   3

Thursday   4

Friday   5

Saturday   6

Sunday   7

S	M	T	W	T	F	S
31	1	2	3	4	5	6
7	8	9	10	11	12	13
14	15	16	17	18	19	20
21	22	23	24	25	26	27
28	29	30	1	2	3	4

"Say... now *I'm* starting to feel kinda warm!"

November

Monday   8

Tuesday   9

Wednesday   10

Thursday   11

Armistice Day
Remembrance Day (Canada)
Veterans' Day (USA)

Friday   12

Saturday   13

Sunday   14

S	M	T	W	T	F	S
31	1	2	3	4	5	6
7	8	9	10	11	12	13
14	15	16	17	18	19	20
21	22	23	24	25	26	27
28	29	30				

"Nik! The fireflies across the street—I think they're mooning us!"

November

Monday   15

Tuesday   16

Wednesday   17

Day of Repentance and Prayer (Germany)

Thursday   18

Friday   19

Saturday   20

S	M	T	W	T	F	S
31	1	2	3	4	5	6
7	8	9	10	11	12	13
14	15	16	17	18	19	20
21	22	23	24	25	26	27
28	29	30	1	2	3	4

Sunday   21

"You idiot! I said get the room freshener! That's the insecticide!"

November

Notes

Monday 22

Tuesday 23

Wednesday 24

Thursday 25

Thanksgiving Day (USA)

Friday 26

Saturday 27

S	M	T	W	T	F	S
31	1	2	3	4	5	6
7	8	9	10	11	12	13
14	15	16	17	18	19	20
21	22	23	24	25	26	27
28	29	30	1	2	3	4

Sunday 28

First Sunday in Advent

December

Sunday	Monday	Tuesday	Wednesday	Thursday	Friday	Saturday
28	29	30	1 First Day of Summer (Southern Hemisphere)	2	3	4 First Day of Chanukah
5	6 Independence Day (Finland)	7	8	9 Ramadan begins	10	11
12	13	14	15	16	17	18
19	20	21	22 Winter Solstice (Northern Hemisphere)	23	24 Christmas Eve	25 Christmas Day
26 Boxing Day Kwanzaa begins (USA)	27 Christmas Day Holiday (Australia, New Zealand, UK)	28 Boxing Day Holiday (Australia, New Zealand, UK)	29	30	31 New Year's Eve	1

Notes

November

S	M	T	W	T	F	S
31	1	2	3	4	5	6
7	8	9	10	11	12	13
14	15	16	17	18	19	20
21	22	23	24	25	26	27
28	29	30				

January 2000

S	M	T	W	T	F	S
						1
2	3	4	5	6	7	8
9	10	11	12	13	14	15
16	17	18	19	20	21	22
23	24	25	26	27	28	29
30	31					

December

Notes

Monday   November 29

Tuesday   30

Wednesday   1

First Day of Summer (Southern Hemisphere)

Thursday   2

Friday   3

Saturday   4

First Day of Chanukah

Sunday   5

S	M	T	W	T	F	S
28	29	30	1	2	3	4
5	6	7	8	9	10	11
12	13	14	15	16	17	18
19	20	21	22	23	24	25
26	27	28	29	30	31	

"Say, Will—why don't you pull that thing out and play us a tune?"

December

Notes

Monday — 6

Independence Day (Finland)

Tuesday — 7

Wednesday — 8

Thursday — 9

Ramadan begins

Friday — 10

Saturday — 11

S	M	T	W	T	F	S
28	29	30	1	2	3	4
5	6	7	8	9	10	11
12	13	14	15	16	17	18
19	20	21	22	23	24	25
26	27	28	29	30	31	

Sunday — 12

The elephant's nightmare

December

Monday   13

Tuesday   14

Wednesday   15

Thursday   16

Friday   17

Saturday   18

Sunday   19

S	M	T	W	T	F	S
28	29	30	1	2	3	4
5	6	7	8	9	10	11
12	13	14	15	16	17	18
19	20	21	22	23	24	25
26	27	28	29	30	31	

December

Monday   20

Tuesday   21

Wednesday   22

Winter Solstice (Northern Hemisphere)

Thursday   23

Friday   24

Christmas Eve

Saturday   25

Christmas Day

Sunday   26

Boxing Day
Kwanzaa begins (USA)

S	M	T	W	T	F	S
28	29	30	1	2	3	4
5	6	7	8	9	10	11
12	13	14	15	16	17	18
19	20	21	22	23	24	25
26	27	28	29	30	31	1

Throughout their songwriting careers, the Gershwins rarely discussed their younger brother, Nathan, who played gutbucket.

December

Monday   27

Christmas Day Holiday
(Australia, New zealand, UK)

Tuesday   28

Boxing Day Holiday
(Australia, New zealand, UK)

Wednesday   29

Thursday   30

Friday   31

New Year's Eve

Saturday

January 2000   1

New Year's Day

Sunday   2

S	M	T	W	T	F	S
28	29	30	1	2	3	4
5	6	7	8	9	10	11
12	13	14	15	16	17	18
19	20	21	22	23	24	25
26	27	28	29	30	31	1

January 2000

February

March

April

_____
_____
_____
_____
_____
_____

May

_____
_____
_____
_____
_____
_____

June

_____
_____
_____
_____
_____
_____

July 2000

August

September

October

November

December

January 1998

S	M	T	W	T	F	S
28	29	30	31	1	2	3
4	5	6	7	8	9	10
11	12	13	14	15	16	17
18	19	20	21	22	23	24
25	26	27	28	29	30	31

February 1998

S	M	T	W	T	F	S
1	2	3	4	5	6	7
8	9	10	11	12	13	14
15	16	17	18	19	20	21
22	23	24	25	26	27	28
1	2	3	4	5	6	7

March 1998

S	M	T	W	T	F	S
1	2	3	4	5	6	7
8	9	10	11	12	13	14
15	16	17	18	19	20	21
22	23	24	25	26	27	28
29	30	31	1	2	3	4

April 1998

S	M	T	W	T	F	S
29	30	31	1	2	3	4
5	6	7	8	9	10	11
12	13	14	15	16	17	18
19	20	21	22	23	24	25
26	27	28	29	30	1	2

May 1998

S	M	T	W	T	F	S
26	27	28	29	30	1	2
3	4	5	6	7	8	9
10	11	12	13	14	15	16
17	18	19	20	21	22	23
24 / 31	25	26	27	28	29	30

June 1998

S	M	T	W	T	F	S
31	1	2	3	4	5	6
7	8	9	10	11	12	13
14	15	16	17	18	19	20
21	22	23	24	25	26	27
28	29	30	1	2	3	4

July 1998

S	M	T	W	T	F	S
28	29	30	1	2	3	4
5	6	7	8	9	10	11
12	13	14	15	16	17	18
19	20	21	22	23	24	25
26	27	28	29	30	31	1

August 1998

S	M	T	W	T	F	S
26	27	28	29	30	31	1
2	3	4	5	6	7	8
9	10	11	12	13	14	15
16	17	18	19	20	21	22
23 / 30	24 / 31	25	26	27	28	29

September 1998

S	M	T	W	T	F	S
30	31	1	2	3	4	5
6	7	8	9	10	11	12
13	14	15	16	17	18	19
20	21	22	23	24	25	26
27	28	29	30	1	2	3

October 1998

S	M	T	W	T	F	S
27	28	29	30	1	2	3
4	5	6	7	8	9	10
11	12	13	14	15	16	17
18	19	20	21	22	23	24
25	26	27	28	29	30	31

November 1998

S	M	T	W	T	F	S
1	2	3	4	5	6	7
8	9	10	11	12	13	14
15	16	17	18	19	20	21
22	23	24	25	26	27	28
29	30	1	2	3	4	5

December 1998

S	M	T	W	T	F	S
29	30	1	2	3	4	5
6	7	8	9	10	11	12
13	14	15	16	17	18	19
20	21	22	23	24	25	26
27	28	29	30	31	1	2

January 1999

S	M	T	W	T	F	S
27	28	29	30	31	1	2
3	4	5	6	7	8	9
10	11	12	13	14	15	16
17	18	19	20	21	22	23
24/31	25	26	27	28	29	30

February 1999

S	M	T	W	T	F	S
31	1	2	3	4	5	6
7	8	9	10	11	12	13
14	15	16	17	18	19	20
21	22	23	24	25	26	27
28	1	2	3	4	5	6

March 1999

S	M	T	W	T	F	S
28	1	2	3	4	5	6
7	8	9	10	11	12	13
14	15	16	17	18	19	20
21	22	23	24	25	26	27
28	29	30	31	1	2	3

April 1999

S	M	T	W	T	F	S
28	29	30	31	1	2	3
4	5	6	7	8	9	10
11	12	13	14	15	16	17
18	19	20	21	22	23	24
25	26	27	28	29	30	1

May 1999

S	M	T	W	T	F	S
25	26	27	28	29	30	1
2	3	4	5	6	7	8
9	10	11	12	13	14	15
16	17	18	19	20	21	22
23/30	24/31	25	26	27	28	29

June 1999

S	M	T	W	T	F	S
30	31	1	2	3	4	5
6	7	8	9	10	11	12
13	14	15	16	17	18	19
20	21	22	23	24	25	26
27	28	29	30	1	2	3

July 1999

S	M	T	W	T	F	S
27	28	29	30	1	2	3
4	5	6	7	8	9	10
11	12	13	14	15	16	17
18	19	20	21	22	23	24
25	26	27	28	29	30	31

August 1999

S	M	T	W	T	F	S
1	2	3	4	5	6	7
8	9	10	11	12	13	14
15	16	17	18	19	20	21
22	23	24	25	26	27	28
29	30	31	1	2	3	4

September 1999

S	M	T	W	T	F	S
29	30	31	1	2	3	4
5	6	7	8	9	10	11
12	13	14	15	16	17	18
19	20	21	22	23	24	25
26	27	28	29	30	1	2

October 1999

S	M	T	W	T	F	S
26	27	28	29	30	1	2
3	4	5	6	7	8	9
10	11	12	13	14	15	16
17	18	19	20	21	22	23
24/31	25	26	27	28	29	30

November 1999

S	M	T	W	T	F	S
31	1	2	3	4	5	6
7	8	9	10	11	12	13
14	15	16	17	18	19	20
21	22	23	24	25	26	27
28	29	30	1	2	3	4

December 1999

S	M	T	W	T	F	S
28	29	30	1	2	3	4
5	6	7	8	9	10	11
12	13	14	15	16	17	18
19	20	21	22	23	24	25
26	27	28	29	30	31	1

January 2000

S	M	T	W	T	F	S
26	27	28	29	30	31	1
2	3	4	5	6	7	8
9	10	11	12	13	14	15
16	17	18	19	20	21	22
23 30	24 31	25	26	27	28	29

February 2000

S	M	T	W	T	F	S
30	31	1	2	3	4	5
6	7	8	9	10	11	12
13	14	15	16	17	18	19
20	21	22	23	24	25	26
27	28	29	1	2	3	4

March 2000

S	M	T	W	T	F	S
27	28	29	1	2	3	4
5	6	7	8	9	10	11
12	13	14	15	16	17	18
19	20	21	22	23	24	25
26	27	28	29	30	31	1

April 2000

S	M	T	W	T	F	S
26	27	28	29	30	31	1
2	3	4	5	6	7	8
9	10	11	12	13	14	15
16	17	18	19	20	21	22
23 30	24	25	26	27	28	29

May 2000

S	M	T	W	T	F	S
30	1	2	3	4	5	6
7	8	9	10	11	12	13
14	15	16	17	18	19	20
21	22	23	24	25	26	27
28	29	30	31	1	2	3

June 2000

S	M	T	W	T	F	S
28	29	30	31	1	2	3
4	5	6	7	8	9	10
11	12	13	14	15	16	17
18	19	20	21	22	23	24
25	26	27	28	29	30	1

July 2000

S	M	T	W	T	F	S
25	26	27	28	29	30	1
2	3	4	5	6	7	8
9	10	11	12	13	14	15
16	17	18	19	20	21	22
23 30	24 31	25	26	27	28	29

August 2000

S	M	T	W	T	F	S
30	31	1	2	3	4	5
6	7	8	9	10	11	12
13	14	15	16	17	18	19
20	21	22	23	24	25	26
27	28	29	30	31	1	2

September 2000

S	M	T	W	T	F	S
27	28	29	30	31	1	2
3	4	5	6	7	8	9
10	11	12	13	14	15	16
17	18	19	20	21	22	23
24	25	26	27	28	29	30

October 2000

S	M	T	W	T	F	S
1	2	3	4	5	6	7
8	9	10	11	12	13	14
15	16	17	18	19	20	21
22	23	24	25	26	27	28
29	30	31	1	2	3	4

November 2000

S	M	T	W	T	F	S
29	30	31	1	2	3	4
5	6	7	8	9	10	11
12	13	14	15	16	17	18
19	20	21	22	23	24	25
26	27	28	29	30	1	2

December 2000

S	M	T	W	T	F	S
26	27	28	29	30	1	2
3	4	5	6	7	8	9
10	11	12	13	14	15	16
17	18	19	20	21	22	23
24 31	25	26	27	28	29	30

Names & Numbers

Names & Numbers